This book belongs to ...

....

OXFORD
UNIVERSITY PRESS

Great Clarendon Street, Oxford, OX2 6DP, United Kingdom

Oxford University Press is a department of the University of Oxford.
It furthers the University's objective of excellence in research, scholarship
and education by publishing worldwide. Oxford is a registered trade mark
of Oxford University Press in the UK and in certain other countries

Run, Run!, The Big Carrot, Lots of Nuts, Get the Rat! first published in 2011
This Edition published in 2013

British Library Cataloguing in Publication Data
Data available

ISBN: 978-0-19-273453-2

10 9 8 7 6 5 4 3 2

Typeset in OUP Earlybird

Printed in China

Paper used in the production of this book is a natural, recyclable product
made from wood grown in sustainable forests. The manufacturing process
conforms to the environmental regulations of the country of origin.

Acknowledgements

Series Advisor: Nikki Gamble

Oxford Reading Tree

Traditional Tales

The Gingerbread Man

and Other Stories

OXFORD

UNIVERSITY PRESS

Tips for reading Run, Run! together

About the story

This story is a simple retelling of 'The Gingerbread Man', which was first printed in 1895 in America in a children's magazine.

This book practises these letter patterns:

s a t p i n m d g o c e u r h b ck

Ask your child to point to these letters or letter pairs and say the sounds.

Your child might find these words tricky:

the I go

Say these words for your child if they do not know them.

- Before you begin, ask your child to read the title to you by sounding out and blending. Talk about what the story might be about. Who might be running and why?

- Encourage your child to read the story to you. Talk about the pictures as you read.

- Your child will be able to read most of the words in the story, but if they struggle with a word, remind them to say the sounds in the word from left to right. Ask them to point to the sounds as they say them, and then blend the sounds into a whole word, e.g. r-u-n, run.

- After you have read the story, look through it again and talk about what happened. How are all of the different characters feeling at the end of the story?

- Do the fun activity together!

Run, Run!

Written by Alex Lane

Illustrated by Paula Metcalf

OXFORD
UNIVERSITY PRESS

8

The cat ran.

Dad ran.

Let's pretend ...

Let's pretend to be the Gingerbread Man and the Fox!

Gingerbread Man

Fox

What are they both saying?

What are they both thinking?

Oh no! Where's the Gingerbread Man gone?

Tips for reading The Big Carrot together

About the story

This story is a simple retelling of 'The Enormous Turnip', which is a Russian or Slavic traditional tale. The story shows the rewards of helping others.

This book practises these letter patterns:

s a t p i m d g o k e u r h b f l ck

Ask your child to point to these letters or letter pairs and say the sounds.

Your child might find these words tricky:

the and

Say these words for your child if they do not know them.

- Before you begin, ask your child to read the title to you by sounding out and blending. Talk about what the story might be about. How big do carrots usually grow?

- Encourage your child to read the story to you. Talk about the pictures as you read.

- Your child will be able to read most of the words in the story, but if they struggle with a word, remind them to say the sounds in the word from left to right. Ask them to point to the sounds as they say them, and then blend the sounds into a whole word, e.g. b-i-g, big.

- After you have read the story, look through it again and ask your child to tell you who helped pull up the big carrot. Can they remember the order the characters joined the line?

- Do the fun activity together!

- Watch this story being performed by a professional storyteller www.oxfordowl.co.uk

The
Big
Carrot

Written by Alison Hawes

Illustrated by Stuart Trotter

OXFORD
UNIVERSITY PRESS

Can Tom get the big carrot?

Tug!

Tom and Ifra
tug the big carrot.

Tom, Ifra and Nick tug.

Tom, Ifra, Nick and Lin tug.

Tom, Ifra, Nick, Lin
and Sam tug.

Tom, Ifra,
Nick, Lin,
Sam and Kit tug.

27

Up pops the big carrot!

Mmmm!

Put them in order

The big carrot needed lots of people to pull it out!

Which picture should go first?

Which picture should go last?

Tips for reading Lots of Nuts together

About the story

This story is a simple retelling of Aesop's fable 'The Town Mouse and the Country Mouse'.

This book practises these letter patterns:

s a t p i m d g o k e u r h
b f l ck ff

Ask your child to point to these letters or letter pairs and say the sounds.

Your child might find these words tricky:

the   I   to

Say these words for your child if they do not know them.

- Before you begin, ask your child to read the title to you by sounding out and blending. Talk about what the story might be about. Who is the mouse in the illustration? Do you think he likes nuts?

- Encourage your child to read the story to you. Talk about the pictures as you read.

- Your child will be able to read most of the words in the story, but if they struggle with a word, remind them to say the sounds in the word from left to right. Ask them to point to the sounds as they say them, and then blend the sounds into a whole word, e.g. o-ff, off; l-o-t-s, lots.

- After you have read the story, look through it again and on page 42 talk about the thought bubble. What is Tim thinking? Did Tim feel differently on page 39?

- Do the fun activity together!

Lots of Nuts

Written by Gill Munton

Illustrated by Emma Dodson

OXFORD
UNIVERSITY PRESS

Tim had lots
of nuts.

Tim

Tom had a big
bag of buns.

38

43

Who likes what?

Can you remember the things that Tim and Tom like?

What do they both like?

What do they both *not* like?

Tips for reading Get the Rat! together

About the story

This story is based on a circular theme, which is a traditional story structure. A rat needs to be caught in the palace. The result is chaos and at the end, it looks as if the whole cycle is about to start again!

This book practises these letter patterns:

s a t p i m d g o k e u r h b

f l s ss ck

Ask your child to point to these letters or letter pairs and say the sounds.

Your child might find this word tricky:

the   Say this word for your child if they do not know it.

- Before you begin, ask your child to read the title to you by sounding out and blending. Talk about what the story might be about. Who might want to get the rat?

- Encourage your child to read the story to you. Talk about the pictures as you read.

- Your child will be able to read most of the words in the story, but if they struggle with a word, remind them to say the sounds in the word from left to right. Ask them to point to the sounds as they say them, and then blend the sounds into a whole word, e.g. r-a-t, rat.

- After you have read the story, look through it again and talk about what happened. Talk about what the rat might be thinking on each page.

- Do the fun activity together!

Get the Rat!

Written by Alex Lane

Illustrated by Sholto Walker

OXFORD
UNIVERSITY PRESS

55

Get the rat!

It is a mess.

That's not a rat!

The princess thought she saw a rat.

What did she see? Can you put them in order?

Is that a rat?

Practise Your Phonics With
Traditional Tales

More stories for you to enjoy...

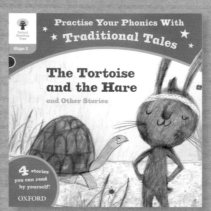

Coming soon...

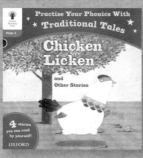

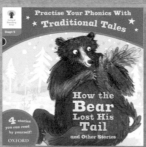

Help your child's learning with essential tips, phonics support and free eBooks

www.oxfordowl.co.uk

62